by Jayneen Sanders   illustrated by Diane Ewen

Who Am I? I AM ME!

A book to explore gender equality, gender stereotyping, acceptance and diversity

Allowing your child to do the things
they love and simply be themselves
is one of the greatest gifts
you can provide.

J.S.

Who Am I? I Am Me!
Educate2Empower Publishing an imprint of
UpLoad Publishing Pty Ltd
Victoria Australia
www.upload.com.au

First published in 2018

Text copyright © Jayneen Sanders 2018
Illustration copyright © UpLoad Publishing Pty Ltd 2018

Written by Jayneen Sanders
Illustrations by Diane Ewen

Jayneen Sanders asserts her right to be identified as the author of this work.

Diane Ewen asserts her right to be identified as the illustrator of this work.

Designed by Stephanie Spartels, Studio Spartels

All rights reserved. No part of this publication may be reproduced, stored in a retrieval system, or transmitted in any way or by any means, electronic, mechanical, photocopying, recording or otherwise, without the prior written permission of UpLoad Publishing Pty Ltd.

ISBN: 9781925089325 (hbk) 9781925089318 (pbk)

A catalogue record for this
book is available from the
National Library of Australia

Disclaimer: The information in this book is advice only written by the author
based on her advocacy in this area, and her experience working with
children as a classroom teacher and mother. The information is not
meant to be a substitute for professional advice. If you are concerned
about a child's behavior seek professional help.

Note from the Author

Children are not born knowing what it means to be a 'boy' or a 'girl'. Gender stereotyping is placed upon them by the adults and older children around them and societal expectations. Gender stereotyping can begin in the womb, i.e. as soon as the expectant parent/s know the sex of their child based on the external organs observed on the ultrasound. Conversations such as, 'Oh! You're having a girl! She is going to be so sweet!' or 'Oh! You're having a boy! He's going to be strong just like his dad' are common. Of course, they don't always happen, but these kinds of conversations do occur regularly.

Once the child is born, the toys he or she is given, the clothes that are chosen and the colors selected often reflect gender stereotyping. In my experience, as a mother and an educator, young children love all toys and all types of activities when allowed to play freely, devoid of gender norms. They will choose games, toys and books based on their interests. Boys will dress up as princesses simply because they love a particular princess from a story or they enjoy the 'swish' of the material. Girls love to dress up as fire-fighters and pirates just as boys do.

However, as children grow, the social expectations of what it is to be 'male' and 'female' become quite rigid. In my observations, many boys tend to push forward and girls tend to take a step back. If we are to progress into a society where gender equality is a given, educators and parents have an important role in breaking down these gender stereotypes and encouraging kids simply to be kids.

The stereotypical language and the rigid gender-assigned roles we so often use are also important, e.g. in the case of a parent (mother), 'Jake can help Dad with the mowing and Kate can help me in the kitchen' or in the case of a teacher, 'Boys can take out the bins and girls can clean the board.' These kinds of expectations are out-dated and do not move us forward towards a more equitable society.

Lastly, children who may come to identify as a gender other than the one assigned to them at birth will be consistent, insistent and persistent about their transgender identity. So just because your son likes to dress up as a princess during 'dress-ups' at school certainly does not mean he is identifying as a transgender person. It simply means he likes to role-play as a princess. Similarly, if your daughter loves to wear a hardhat and help with building jobs around the house, this does not mean she identifies as a 'boy'. It simply means she loves building things. Allowing your child to do the things they love and be who they are is one of the greatest gifts you can provide. This book has been written to open up a conversation with children about their own individual preferences for toys, activities, games, books, etc. and to break down gender norms. In the long run, if we eliminate gender stereotyping there will be more choices for all genders, the likelihood of one gender believing they have power of another will be lessened, and children growing into adults will be free to follow their passions and be truly who they are. I hope you and the children in your care enjoy this book and the discussions it will bring.

Hi! My name is Frankie. This book will tell you lots about me. And people will learn lots about you too!

You are you,
and I am me.
We are whoever
we want to be!

I like building things with my mama and my dad.

I have my own tool belt with a hammer
and a screwdriver.

Sometimes I have to wear a hardhat —
just like Mama and Dad.

Bang!
Bang!

Do you like
building things?
What kinds of
things do you build?

Our baby's name is Maccy.

She is ten months old.

She drinks milk from Mama.

Sometimes I help Dad
change her nappy.

When I grow up I might want a baby or
I might want a kitten instead.

Or maybe I will have both!

Do you have a baby
in your home?
What do you do
to help?

I love trains! I have 2 engines and 10 carriages.
My trains go round and round the track.

Toot!
Toot!

Sometimes I put 1, 2, 3, 4, 5, 6, 7, 8, 9, 10 carriages on the big blue engine.

What is your favorite toy to play with? Why do you like it?

I like playing dress-ups at school. We have a big red box.
In the box there are sparkly dresses and pirate hats.
There's a fire-fighter's uniform and an astronaut's suit.
Sometimes I dress up as a fire-fighter. And sometimes
I dress up as a princess. And sometimes I
dress up as both!

Do you like
playing dress-ups?
What do you
like to dress-up as?

I love the doll corner at school too! My friends and I take care of the dolls. We tuck them into their beds and sing 'Hush-a-bye Baby'. Sometimes we carry them in a sling until they fall fast asleep.

Do you have a
favorite doll?
What games do
you like to play
with your doll?

15

When I go to Grandma's house we cook pancakes.
Grandma says we make the best pancakes in the world.

Yum!
Yum!

I like to eat pancakes
with butter and honey.

What do you like
to cook? Who helps
you when you cook?

At the school fair this year we had pony rides.

I rode a pony called Ginger. Ginger had soft orange hair and big brown eyes. Ginger was the perfect size for me!

Have you been to
a school fair?
What was the
best thing at the fair?

Sometimes Mama takes me to the climbing wall near her work. It's really hard to get to the top but I always keep trying.

I CAN do this!

What is something that is hard for you to do?

For my birthday last year I went on a steam train.
It was so much fun. The train went

Chug! Chug! Chug! Toot! Toot!

I waved to all the cars
passing by.

What do you like to do on your birthday?

23

When we go camping in the spring, my friend and I build little houses for the fairy folk. We make sure we put lots of leaves and moss inside, so the fairy folk are cozy and warm.

What do you like to do in the spring?

I love to play soccer with my friends. We play after school and on the weekends. I am a really fast runner — just like my friend, Zara.

What things are
you good at?
What sports do
you like to play?

My grandpa lives in a home with lots of other old people.
When I visit Grandpa I read books and draw him pictures.
I always bring my tea set so I can make Grandpa
a cup of tea.

Do you visit
any older people?
What do you talk
to them about?

At bedtime I love to read books. I like stories about dinosaurs, fairies and space travel. Sometimes Mama reads to me and sometimes I read all by myself.

What kind of
stories do you like?
Do you read with
someone or by yourself?

Now you know lots about me, I am going to
ask you three questions.

1. Am I a boy?

2. Am I a girl?

3. Who am I?

I am ME!

Discussion Questions for Parents, Caregivers and Educators

The following Discussion Questions are intended as a guide and can be used to initiate an important dialogue with your child around diversity, acceptance, inclusion and the fact that everyone has the right to be who they want to be — regardless of which gender they identify with. The questions are optional and/or can be explored at different readings. I suggest you allow your child time to answer the questions both on the internal pages and in this section, as well as encouraging them to ask their own questions around this important topic.

Pages 4–5

What is Frankie wearing? Why do you think Frankie is wearing a hat and a tiger suit? What do you think, 'You are you' and 'I am me' means? Can you be whatever you want to be? Why do you say that?

Pages 6–7

What do you like to build? Do you have tools and a hardhat like Frankie? Why do you think people wear hardhats/tool belts when they are building things?

Pages 8–9

Why do you think babies need to drink milk? Why do you think Frankie looks a little bit unhappy as Dad changes Maccy's nappy? Who changed your nappy when you were a baby? Would you like a baby brother or sister?

Why do you say that? Do you think you might want a baby when you grow up? Why do you say that?

Pages 10–11

What are your favorite things to do and play? Do you like playing with trains? Why do you say that?

Pages 12–13

What is the girl dressed up as? What about this boy? And this girl? And this boy? If you could choose from this dress-up box, what would you wear? Why do you say that? Is it okay for a girl to dress up as a pirate? Is it okay for a boy to dress up as a princess? Why do you say that? When girls/boys grow up, can they become astronauts/fire-fighters/magicians/pirates? Why do you say that?

Pages 14–15

Do you like playing with dolls? Why do you say that? Do you have a doll corner at home/school? Can you tell me about your doll corner?

Pages 16–17

Why might Frankie like to go to Grandma's house? Do you have a grandma? What things do you like to do at your grandma's house? Do you like to eat pancakes? What do you like to put on top of your pancakes?

Pages 18–19

Does your school have a fair? What things do they have at the fair? What is the lady on page 18 doing? What shape has been painted onto the boy's/girl's face? Have you ever had your face painted? What shape was painted onto your face? Have you ever ridden a pony? What was it like? Do you think Frankie is enjoying riding Ginger? How can you tell?

Pages 20–21

Have you ever tried to climb a climbing wall? Was it hard to do? Why is it important to always keep trying when something becomes hard to do?

Pages 22–23

Why do you think Frankie wanted to go on a steam train for a birthday celebration? Have you ever been on a steam train? Did you enjoy the ride? Why/Why not? Would you like to be the driver of a steam train? Why do you say that?

Pages 24–25

Have you ever made fairy houses? What did you use to make them? Have you ever been camping? Who did you go with? Was it fun when you went camping? What things did you do? How did you help?

Pages 26–27

Have you ever played soccer? What did you like about playing soccer?

Pages 28–29

Why do you think Frankie's grandpa likes Frankie's visits? Do you have a grandfather/grandpa? What things do you like to do together? Do you have a tea set? Can you tell me about your tea set? Do you think older people get lonely sometimes? Why do you say that?

Pages 30–31

What is your favorite thing in Frankie's room? Why do you say that? Do you think Frankie has lots of books? Why do you say that? Who do you like to read stories with?

Pages 32–33

Ask the first question: 'Am I a boy?' If your child says 'yes' ask why they think that. If your child says 'no' ask the second question, and then ask why your child thinks that. Ask the third question. Your child may choose to answer or not. I suggest you turn the page quite quickly.

Pages 34–35

Focus on the fact that Frankie is his/her own individual self and it doesn't matter if he/she is a girl or a boy; Frankie is simply a person who loves all kinds of things that traditionally could have been gender specific but are no longer. Review the rhyme on page 5 with your child and talk about how this rhyme relates to them personally.

Gender-neutral Parenting and Teaching Tips

Gender stereotyping begins as soon as the child's gender is known. However, once you 'see' gender stereotyping in society you can't 'un-see' it!

- From day one, provide your daughter with spatial developmental toys, books where girls are the heroes and have adventures, clothes that reflect the colors and styles she likes not the color and styles society dictates for girls. And yes, provide her with dolls, a baby sling and kitchen sets for cooking but provide exactly the same toys and resources for your son! The key word here is choice. Provide your child, no matter what gender they identify as, with choice so we nurture a society where gender does not determine how anyone is treated.

- Keep in mind as you parent we are all more the same than we are different. Focus on our 'sameness' rather than our differences. Help your child to understand we have a human commonality — everyone feels, and everyone has hopes and dreams. Our gender should and needs to be irrelevant. A great practical activity is to look at a page from this book or another children's book where there is a male and a female character. List what is the same and what is different between the characters and have a discussion with your child. Children will soon come to realize that there is more the same between the genders than there is different, e.g. we all have hands, arms, eyes, etc. Of course, every child is their own unique self and we need to nurture and encourage this, but in regards to gender the only real difference is small aspects of our physiology.

- Provide equal opportunities for all children to follow their passions. If your son likes to cook — nurture that passion. If your daughter wants to play and follow football — provide the opportunity for her to do so.

- As parents, caregivers and educators the language we use is also crucial, i.e. refrain from using language such as 'that's a boy's sport' or 'only girls play with dolls', etc. This kind of unhelpful, outdated and gender-based language only reinforces gender norms and the power imbalance.

- Sadly, the current stereotypes that we see in the media and online (TV, music, films, books, etc.) are very problematic and if big business continues to market specifically for girls and boys, gender-based norms will only become more ingrained. Our girls will see little choice other than pink and 'cute' in the girls' section of a store, and our boys will see no other choice than blue or gray and 'rough and tumble' in the boys' section. Consequently, and sadly, this is what they become as gender stereotyping continues to be reinforced every hour of every day online, in stores, on TV, in video games, in songs, in books, etc. And because many adults in these children's lives see and perpetuate the same messages, gender stereotyping continues to be reinforced in our homes and classrooms. However, now is the perfect time for parents and educators to push back and see how gender stereotyping is limiting children's and ultimately society's possibilities. When gender stereotyping is obvious use this opportunity to unpack it with the children in your care.

Quick Tips

• Give all children choices. • Do not reinforce traditional gender roles in your home or classroom, i.e. boys can take the bins out and girls can do the dishes. • Treat both boys and girls as equally strong and empowered, and encourage them all to have a voice. • Let both boys and girls know it's okay to express and discuss feelings and emotions, and to cry when they are sad. • Offer a range of toys and activities to children that are non-gender specific. • Do not use gender-specific language that reinforces gender norms e.g. 'only girls can have their face painted as a butterfly'. • Take kids aside for a discussion when they say things such as 'Jess can't play with us because it's a boy's game'; use such a scenario as the perfect teaching opportunity. • Never stereotype children's traits, e.g. boys are loud and noisy, girls are calm and sweet, and call out relatives and teachers who do so. • Monitor your own interactions with boys and girls and comfort a boy as you would a girl if they are sad or unhappy. • When reading books, change the characters around, e.g. change the tiger from 'he' to 'she' and the butterfly from 'she' to 'he'. • Discuss traditional male and female employment roles and show kids images of the opposite, e.g. a woman fire-fighter, a woman astronaut, etc. • Use non-gender specific terms when referring to occupations, e.g. chairperson, flight attendant, police officer. • Encourage girls in particular to pursue their interest in science. • Encourage our young men, in particular, to speak out when they see sexist behaviors and tell other young men this is not okay.

Finally …

I believe it's up to the adults in children's lives to shape and nurture a change in attitudes. If the adults in a child's life continue to reinforce gender stereotyping then gender inequality will continue to exist, and that is very unhealthy for society as a whole. We know in family and domestic violence incidences, one person believes they have power over another and uses that power for physical, mental, emotional and/or sexual abuse. We need to teach children from a young age that all genders are equal and no gender has legitimate power over another.

Educators, parents and caregivers can play a major role in pushing back against gender norms. Children are not born thinking one gender is better and more powerful than another. They are born thinking there is no difference between boys and girls. Hopefully, I have outlined some simple but effective ways adults can help to break down gender stereotyping resulting in a more equitable society. Our children need to grow up knowing all people are equal and to respect each other for who they are regardless of gender, race, culture or religion.

Books by the Same Author

Talking About Feelings

A book to assist adults in helping children unpack, understand and manage their feelings and emotions in an engaging and interactive way. Discussion Questions included.
Ages 4 to 10 years.

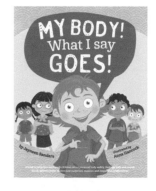

My Body! What I Say Goes!

A children's picture book to empower and teach children about personal body safety, feelings, safe and unsafe touch, private parts, secrets and surprises, consent and respect. Discussion Questions included. Ages 3 to 9 years.

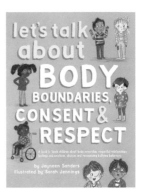

Let's Talk About Body Boundaries, Consent and Respect

Through familiar scenarios, this book opens up crucial conversations with children around body boundaries, consent and respect. Discussion Questions included.
Ages 4 to 10 years.

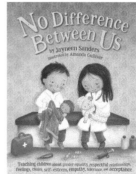

No Difference Between Us

Jess is a girl and Ben is a boy but in all the BIG ways there is no difference between them. A story to explore gender equality, respectful relationships, feelings and self-esteem. Discussion Questions included.
Ages 2 to 9 years.

Pearl Fairweather, Pirate Captain

Through an engaging narrative, this beautifully illustrated children's book explores gender equality, respect, diversity, leadership, and recognizing bullying behaviors. Discussion Questions included.
Ages 5 to 12 years.

You, Me and Empathy

This charming story uses verse, beautiful illustrations and a little person called Quinn to model the meaning of empathy, kindness and compassion. Discussion Questions and activities to promote empathy and kindness included.
Ages 3 to 9 years.

No Means No!

A story about an empowered little girl with a strong voice on all issues, especially those relating to her body! A book to teach children about personal body boundaries, respect and consent. Discussion Questions included. Ages 2 to 9 years.

How Big Are Your Worries Little Bear?

This book was written to help children overcome fears and anxious thoughts by providing them with life-long skills in how to deal with anxiety. Discussion Questions and hints to help anxious children included.
Ages 3 to 9 years.

For more information go to: www.e2epublishing.info

CPSIA information can be obtained
at www.ICGtesting.com
Printed in the USA
LVHW070030100419
613594LV00006B/14/P